Ned and Kit ar_____ _o
spend the day __ __ ____.

Who will they see first?

There are lots of animals for them to visit.

Who is coming too?

First they see some cows munching on green grass.

Who is in the mud?

Then a beautiful pony jumping and skipping.

Where does she sleep?

Some snuffling pigs
in their muddy sty.

Who has a scruffy hat?

Five black sheep peeping over the wall.

Where is the sheep dog?

A scruffy scarecrow in a field of yellow corn.

Who will cut the corn?

Two geese in a pond.
A hen is walking by.

Whose face is this?

A farmer in a red combine harvester.

Where is the cat sleeping?

Some hens and a mouse in the barn.

Who has gone for a walk?

All the animals in the farmyard.

What is Puppy thinking?

Ned, Kit and Puppy have had such fun.

Time to go home!